GCSE English Frames:

Genre

Keith Brindle

Folens Publishers

Contents

Editor: Helen Banbury   Layout artist: Suzanne Ward
Cover design: Ed Gallagher

© 2000 Folens Limited, on behalf of the author.

Every effort has been made to contact copyright holders of material used in this book. If any have been overlooked, we will be pleased to make any necessary arrangements.

British Library Cataloguing in Publication Data. A catalogue record for this book is available from the British Library.

First published 2000 by Folens Limited, Dunstable.
Folens Limited, Albert House, Apex Business Centre, Boscombe Road, Dunstable, LU5 4RL, England.

ISBN 1 84163 582–0

Printed in Singapore by Craft Print.

Introduction

The National Curriculum English Document, upon which all English GCSE examination syllabuses are predicated, insists that all students should experience a wide range of different types of reading and writing. This book aims to help teachers to give students strategies and scaffolding to support their efforts to compose their writing at exam level. The frames enable the least and most able to make more focused use of their skills as readers and writers, by giving them a scaffold, which can be taken away when they are more robust and confident in their own abilities. In essence, it makes the most able answer the specific question, while giving the least able a secure framework within which to locate their own ideas and efforts.

It is, however, the students in the mid-range of ability who stand to gain most from this book. They invariably lack the discourse structures and markers, which are too often taken for granted. This book supplies those markers; gives other pointers as to how various types of writing differ; and develops confidence through adopting good practice.

Each Unit contains five sheets:

Sheet 1: **Key Points and Advice**
This sheet provides a quick check-list of ideas, advice and skills required for the particular form of writing.

Sheet 2: **Practising a Skill**
This sheet focuses on a particular element of exam technique, such as planning, and provides tests to practise this skill.

Sheet 3: **Improving the Content**
This sheet provides ideas for content, plus key phrases or discourse markers which form part of the writer's 'palette', from which students can pick the best words possible.

Sheet 4: **A Writing Frame**
This sheet provides the actual frame for the essay, with key markers and phrases already included.

Sheet 5: **Further Practice**
This sheet provides a model answer with some text omitted for weaker students, or for reinforcement work.

There is an optional disk (PC format) which is for student and teacher use. It contains the same key elements and sheets as the book itself, but has additional features, which will be of use to many students, particularly those who find extended writing difficult, or struggle to employ the ideas required for each piece of coursework or exam task.

The disk contains:
- further tasks for extended practice in the key writing areas
- help with completing these further tasks (word-banks, possible ideas, etc.).

Teacher input
Teachers can also modify the tasks and text, according to the needs and abilities of their students. They might also wish to alter text to suit a particular task that has been practised in class, or delete a line they find unhelpful. Additionally, they can add extra lines of advice or key points that come up during the work. However, there is no necessity to do this, as the disk is designed to be used by students as it stands – and any modification is entirely at the discretion of the teacher concerned.

Printing
A key feature of the disk is the capacity for students to print out their finished work from the 'Frames' pages. When they do so, the boxes will disappear, leaving continuous prose text.

Finally, the disk provides a useful resource for students who will benefit from the extra features it offers, and stimulates their own enthusiasm for using a keyboard and screen for English work. Of course, it is recognised that computer-generated work has limitations for assessment purposes, but it can be a key factor in building skills and scaffolding ideas.

How to install the program
For Windows 95 and 98, put Disk 1 into drive A:. From the Start button, go to Run. At the prompt, type A:\Setup and press Return/Enter. Once Disk 1 has downloaded, you will be asked to replace Disk 1 with Disk 2.
NB If you already have Toolbook software on your computer, you will not need Disk 2.

 *Newspaper Reports*

Key Points and Advice

Newspaper reports usually tell:

◆ the whole story
◆ a clear story.

They generally include:

◆ only information that is relevant
◆ only the names of people important to the story.

They leave the readers feeling they understand what has happened.

Read the following points carefully before you apply them to the given title or exam question.

1. Filter and organise the details, so the important ones are **clear** and in an **order which makes sense**. This is likely to be the chronological order: the order in which things happened.
2. Decide which people and what details about them should be included. Often, you will include just their name, age and occupation or relevance to the story:
   e.g. 'Benjamin Christopher, 16, a building worker, was found …'
       'Nahida Dalvi, 79, who lived next door to the couple, said …'
3. Do not assume the reader already knows what you are writing about.
4. Organise your layout: columns, space for headlines, pictures, captions, etc.
5. Create a headline which draws the reader's attention; and a sub-headline, if appropriate.
6. Write a first paragraph which summarises the story:
   ● what happened?
   ● when?
   ● where?
   ● to whom?
   ● and, possibly, why?
7. Throughout, concentrate on writing about facts.
8. Make sure you write in:
   ● Standard English, unless you are quoting what someone has said
   ● paragraphs – but avoid the temptation to use one-sentence paragraphs!
9. As you write the report, use sub-headings.
10. End by saying what point the story has reached at the time the newspaper was printed. Do not forget that some stories run for days or weeks: more information about your story might be in the next edition (e.g. a murder investigation or a war story). However, you could be writing about a story which now appears finished (e.g. a motorway crash or the capture of an escaped lion).

 **Newspaper Reports**

Practising Organisation

Name: _____ Date: _____

Read this statement, taken from a woman who witnessed a violent assault. Then, put the details into the order you would use for your newspaper report.

I'd seen him hanging around a lot. They said his name was Mark Gold. He was forty years old but acted like a teenage hooligan. He was always in the shopping centre and looked like trouble. He didn't have a job. And he drank too much. Once, I saw him pick on a young mother, swearing at her; and her kids were with her too. Anyway, last Friday I saw him with a bottle of whisky and he was drunk out of his head. Someone said he's been in The Red Lion since it opened. Then he got into this argument with his brother, who's a traffic warden. I think he hated traffic wardens, even though he didn't have a car. I'd seen him shouting at them before. But this time, he went berserk and hit his brother over the head with the bottle. The man fell to the floor and his hat came off and he was bleeding. Gold just laughed and staggered away. I'm not surprised Gold's wife left him last year. I reckon she was lucky to escape. Thank God they've arrested him!

Order for Newspaper Report

1. Mark Gold, 40 years old, unemployed, attacked traffic warden.

2. His wife left him last year.

3.

4.

5.

6.

7.

8.

9.

10.

11.

12. He is now in police custody.

GCSE English Frames: Genre

 *Newspaper Reports*

Newspaper Style

Name: _____ Date: _____

1. Headlines

Headlines are:
- intended to catch the attention of the reader
- often in bold type.

For tabloid newspapers in particular, headlines often contain:
- alliteration – words beginning with the same letter
- puns – words or phrases with more than one meaning:
  - e.g. **Rock star Rita growing bolder!**
    Nottinghamshire worker has Notts in stitches

2. Opening Paragraphs

To begin a newspaper report, it is essential to tell the reader what has happened.

The paragraph must be:
- short
- detailed
- 'punchy'
- easy to understand:
  - e.g. 'There was uproar in Worksop, Nottinghamshire, yesterday when office worker Robert Pressley, 46, ran naked through the town centre, wearing only a baseball cap and a smile.'

3. Sub-headings

When these are used, every few paragraphs, they indicate what the next paragraph or paragraphs will be about. They are often shortened sentences, or phrases:
- e.g. **All for a bet**
  Police not amused

4. Discourse Markers

To help the paragraphs flow smoothly, it is necessary to use linking words and phrases, such as:

later that morning ...   *however ...*
a neighbour confirmed the   *despite ...*
fact that ...   *unfortunately ...*
according to the police ...   *although ...*
because ...
it is thought that ...

5. Final Paragraphs

The reader must be left with a clear understanding of the current situation:
- e.g. 'The police said last night that Mr Pressley had been released on bail. He is expected to appear in court in the next few days. A friend was keen to point out that Mr Pressley will almost certainly be fully clothed when he goes in front of the magistrates.'

GCSE English Frames: Genre

 *Newspaper Reports*

A Writing Frame

Name: _____ Date: _____

Write a report on the story of Mark Gold, using the frame below. Invent any additional information you wish to use.

Mothers and children were shocked

The victim, who had not spoken to his brother for some months

Police confirmed last night

The injured man was taken

It seems he was waiting for his brother

Gold has been charged with assault

Newspaper Reports

A Model Report

Name: _____   Date: _____

Fill in the missing words or phrases in this report.

Ex-boxer has too many rounds

Traffic warden's   shocks shoppers.

Mothers and children in Exmouth were shocked yesterday afternoon, when a man _____ his brother, a traffic warden, with a bottle. Mark Gold, 40, was later arrested _____ with assault.

Victim Stephen Gold

Increasing violence

The victim, who had not spoken to his brother for some months, had given a home to Gold's wife, Stephanie, and _____. She left her husband, an ex-heavyweight boxer, after he became _____. However, _____ Gold held his brother responsible for the breakdown of his marriage.

Police _____ last night that Gold had attacked his wife on two occasions in the previous weeks. Each time he was drunk, but _____ refused to press charges.

Apparently, Gold spent _____ drinking with friends in The Red Lion pub. The landlord, James Reeves, said, "Mark Gold was _____ and I threw him out after he broke the juke box."

Waiting for brother

Gold was spotted outside, drinking from a whisky bottle. _____ waiting for his brother, who worked in the town as a _____ warden.

When Stephen Gold arrived, his brother became foul-mouthed and _____. Stephen Gold was eventually pushed to the ground, at which point he was struck repeatedly _____ whisky bottle.

The injured man was taken _____. He was unconscious when an ambulance arrived; and it is feared he might have suffered brain _____.

Charged

Gold has been charged with assault. He was found and _____ in a nearby park and arrested by police within an hour.

He is being held in custody. His wife was _____, but is known to have taken her children to their grandmother's house.

GCSE English Frames: Genre

 *Magazine Articles*

Key Points and Advice

Magazine articles should:

◆ present a situation or argument in a way that is easy to understand
◆ be organised
◆ consider points of view on any issue discussed
◆ be suitable for the target audience.

They include:

◆ relevant information
◆ interviews if appropriate
◆ a conclusion that usually invites the reader to make a decision on the issue or re-states the viewpoint of the writer.

Read the following points carefully before you apply them to the given title or exam question.

1. Facts and opinions for inclusion should be organised into a sensible plan.
2. This plan should flow logically from an opening to a conclusion.
3. As with newspaper articles, consider layout: columns, pictures, text boxes containing information, etc.
4. Use a headline that is memorable.
5. The first paragraph should:
   ● introduce the subject under discussion
   ● indicate the point of view you will be taking in the article.
6. Ensure you use language that is suitable for your audience. For example:
   ● for a teenage magazine, you might mention 'dance tracks'
   ● for an older audience, 'disco records' might be more suitable
   ● for old folk, you might choose 'music for dancing'.
7. Make the article more 'reader-friendly' by using sub-headings.
8. Quote from relevant people, when appropriate, but *use* the quotations; don't simply let one person's words become your entire article. Quote, then move on.
9. Make sure you remain 'on task' and do not wander from your topic and purpose: e.g. if you write about the problems of teenage pregnancies, discuss sex education in school but *not* why some people are bored by school assemblies. Use only relevant details.
10. End with:
    either
    a statement of your own beliefs
    or
    both sides of a situation, for the reader to consider.

Practising Planning

Name: _____ Date: _____

Write an article for a magazine aimed at parents. Argue that parents should not tell teenagers what to do.

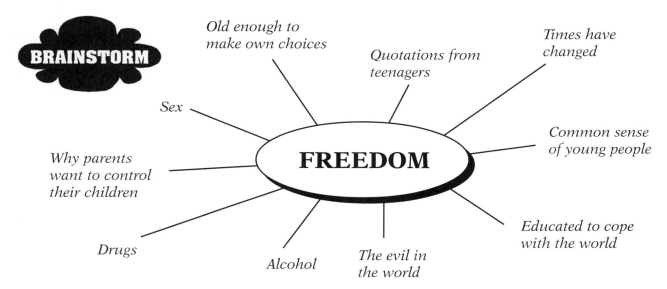

BRAINSTORM

Old enough to make own choices

Quotations from teenagers

Times have changed

Sex

FREEDOM

Common sense of young people

Why parents want to control their children

Drugs

Alcohol

The evil in the world

Educated to cope with the world

Task 1: Add any ideas of your own to the spider diagram.

Task 2: Put the ideas into the order you would deal with them in your article.
(Try putting the points **against** freedom first, then the points **for** freedom.)

1. The evil in the world.

2.

3.

4.

5.

6.

7.

8.

9.

10.

 **Magazine Articles**

Effective Articles

Name: _____ Date: _____

1. Headlines

Make your headline appropriate for the task:

either
- suitably serious (e.g. 'No future for the starving')

or
- humorous (e.g. 'My daughter gave up TV: she's soap-less!').

2. Openings

Often, a challenging opening can make the reader pay attention to the article.

Consider:
- a series of rhetorical questions (which you do not expect the reader to answer but sound challenging).
  E.g. Why do governments spend money on space exploration? Surely there are better things to do with the cash? Wouldn't it be better spent on education? How can they justify wasting it when people are starving all round the world?

or:
- a vivid description.
  E.g. Imagine you are starving in Africa. You have not eaten for days, and your children are crying at your feet. Under such circumstances, the sky is just a burning arch overhead. You do not care whether another spaceship has been launched. You look up in the simple hope that there might be a plane bringing food.

3. Facts and Opinions

Effective articles will often blend relevant facts, which can be proven, with persuasive opinions, which are what the writer believes. Sometimes, these are placed in boxes within the text.

Within them, information is:
- clear
- easy to locate.

4. Endings

Possible endings include:
- statements that stress the writer's viewpoint: e.g. It is clear that we must use the nation's money more sensibly …
- rhetorical questions to which there is likely to be only one answer: e.g. In these circumstances, can there be any doubt about what we should do?
- a final image to touch the reader's emotions:
  e.g. Even if we can forget the horror of life in so many other countries, we cannot forget what is happening closer to home. When we see a homeless person, we know that things should be better. We know that she could be helped. The money that is being wasted could save her life.

 *Magazine Articles*

A Writing Frame

Name: _____   Date: _____

Write an article for a magazine aimed at adults. Argue that teenagers should be allowed the freedom to make their own mistakes.

It is, sadly, a fact that most parents cannot accept that their children grow up

The world is very different from the one their parents knew as teenagers

Parents, of course, say

What teenagers Say:

-
-
-

Nevertheless, you can get married at 16. You must, then, be an adult

There are certain things that parents need to realise

What teenagers think:

-
-
-

It is essential that teenagers are given more freedom because

---

GCSE English Frames: Genre   © Folens (copiable page)

 *Magazine Articles*

A Model Article

Name: _____ Date: _____

Fill in the missing words or phrases in this article.

Set your children   !

It is, sadly, a fact that most   cannot accept the fact that their children grow up.

When a child becomes a teenager, he or she   about the world. It is no longer acceptable for a parent to say, "I know   ." Teenagers must be given the freedom to make their own decisions and   their own mistakes.

Parents, of course, say that there is evil in the   and that young people must be protected. Parents fear   , AIDS and violence. They know the   caused by alcohol and the attraction of sex.

Mature enough

Nevertheless, you can get married at 16, so you must be an adult. And teenagers know they are   enough to cope with the big   world.

In our survey of teenagers:

- 93% say parents don't   them
- 89% believe this causes arguments
- 65% think parents treat them
- 32% say they are 'grounded' unfairly
- 77% feel they   be given more freedom

Teenagers can look after themselves. Common sense and a   of the modern world allows them to make   decisions than their parents realise. For example, at school they have been   about the harmful effects of drugs; and   tell them what it is like 'on the streets'.

The truth about teenagers:

-                do not take drugs
- most do not get drunk
- most want to make parents   of them
- most want to make the world a   place.

The world has changed

The world is very different from the one their parents knew as   . "I think I know more about contraception than my mum," said Julie (14). Her friend Lucy added, "My dad just lives in the   Age. He wouldn't last a minute in any   at my school."

There are certain things that parents need to realise. First, teenagers are no   from what they ever were – they just live in a different society. Second, as we start a new   , they expect to be treated with more respect.

It is essential that teenagers are given more freedom,   otherwise they might simply begin to take it. Would you be happy with an empty bedroom in your house and an   place at your table? As a   parent, you can make   you avoid that tragedy.

Informal Letters

Key Points and Advice

Informal letters usually have:

◆ an appropriate layout
◆ a friendly tone.

They might include:

◆ personal details
◆ a maximum of two or three detailed incidents.

Read the following points carefully before you apply them to the given title or exam question.

1. Put your own address in the top right hand corner. (Do not include your name.)
2. Beneath that, write the date. If it is in full, rather than in numbers, it makes a good impression.
3. 'Dear ...' goes on the next line, against the left hand margin. The body of the letter begins on the line underneath.
4. The first paragraph should be friendly and explain why you are writing.
   E.g.

79 Barnard Street
Healey
Rochmouth
DV14 4LC

16 September 2000

Dear Jeannie,
I was really upset to hear your latest news. What has happened to your mother is terrible. However, did you know that something similar happened to me some years ago? I fell down the stairs because my little brother left a toy car right in my way. So I'm in a perfect position to tell you what the doctors are likely to do ...

5. The content of the letter should be planned in a logical order, as with any piece of writing.
6. Use humour or surprise to keep the reader interested.
7. Do not write too much and lose control of the content and the language.
8. End the letter informally: e.g. 'Love,' (for family and close friends) or 'Best wishes,' (in other cases).
9. Sign your first name underneath.
10. Any 'PS' should be very brief and only mention something important that you have forgotten. If the letter has been properly planned, there should be no need for a 'PS'!

Informal Letters

Practising Beginnings

Name: _____ Date: _____

Write a letter to your aunt who is in hospital. Aim to cheer her up.

Task 1
- Write down **three** important things you might tell her about.
- Make brief notes that indicate the details you will include.

Item 1:
Details:

Item 2:
Details:

Item 3:
Details:

Task 2
- Put your address and the date, then begin your letter.
- Write the first paragraph, mentioning:
  - your sympathy for your aunt
  - why you are writing
  - what you will be talking about in the letter.

 *Informal Letters*

Improving the Content

Name: _____   Date: _____

Writing a good letter is difficult. You must keep:
- the reader interested
- the letter structured.

Don't write about anything you can think of, in any order. Instead, write clearly about just two or three items. Detailed writing is the most effective.

When writing this sort of letter, you can write informally, using, for example:
- 'I've' instead of 'I have'
- 'should've' instead of 'should have'.

In addition, you might use:

1. Humour

Jokes might not be out of place in an informal letter.

If you use them, ensure they:
- are appropriate to what you are writing about
- do not cause offence to the reader.

Anecdotes – little stories about yourself or others – are likely to enliven your letter.

E.g. It really upset me, because I was embarrassed and that doesn't happen very often. Do you remember when we were at primary school and I ended up with my foot stuck down the toilet? Even then, all I did was laugh – especially when the headmistress said that if I ever wanted a part-time job, she would employ me as a toilet brush ...

2. Surprise

Many letters contain only everyday matters: the health of the cat, who is in love with whom, the weather, and so on. If you can introduce more surprising details, your letter is likely to be more interesting.

You might wish to use expressions like:
- You'll never guess what happened when ...
- I've never seen anything like it before, but ...
- It was the most amazing thing I've ever seen ...

3. The Ending

When you reach the end, you should be able to **sum up** what you have said: e.g. That's it, then! As you now know, I'm in love again; the dog has been allowed to sleep in the living room despite what my dad threatened; and Sam did have head lice after all.

*Then, **finish your letter** warmly, using phrases like:*
- I hope you're well and look forward to hearing from you soon.
- Be sure to write back!
- We're all missing you, so let us know how you are.
- Give my love to ... and make sure you get in touch soon.

 GCSE English Frames: Genre   © Folens (copiable page)

 *Informal Letters*

A Writing Frame

Name: _____ Date: _____

Use the following frame to write a letter to your pen-friend, who is coming to stay. Describe what your family is like.

Dear

Thanks for your letter

When you arrive, you'll have to get used to

Of course, that's not all. There is also

Next, there's

Still, I know you will love

Anyway, you'll be arriving soon

A Model Letter

Name: _____ Date: _____

Fill in the missing words or phrases in this letter.

Dear   ,

Thanks for your   . I'm pleased you are   , and even more pleased that you are coming
to stay next   . We'll pick you up at the station, but you had better
yourself for my dad's   driving!

You'll find my dad is rather   , to say the least. He's obsessed with
from the Seventies, and I don't think he's ever   out of the styles either. You'll never have
met anyone like him before. He's   got platform shoes in his wardrobe and he sings Abba
songs in the   . Worse still, he seems to think that Bob Monkhouse is the greatest
comedian. Is that sad, or what?

Mum is much more   , though she's still about a hundred   out of date on most things.
I can tell her all sorts about my life, and she seems like a friend, then she suddenly   she's a
parent and gets all confused about what she should say. I   if it was left to her, I'd get
permission to stay out much later and much more   . Unfortunately, dad wouldn't   to
that. I can only suppose that life was pretty dangerous back in the 70s and he thinks it   is!

Mind you, I get much more   than my little sister. They keep her chained to the house.
Well, not literally chained, but   . The only thing they   her do is have hordes
of her friends over for slumber   . It's awful. They scream and giggle all night and
too many sweets. Then, in the morning they are all   and grumpy. They usually look as if
they've   in the garden.

Dad amuses himself by   those Bob Monkhouse-type jokes like: "What do you call
a deer that can't see anything?" – "No eye deer". I'm   everybody has heard every one of
his jokes before and didn't even laugh the first   . When you get here, just smile now and then,
it will   him happy.

Anyway, you'll be   soon, so we'll find out if you can cope with all of us. Don't forget to
let me   exactly what time your train will   . Also, remember to pass on my best
                    to your family. It was kind of them to send the CD voucher   my birthday.

Bye for now!
Love,

GCSE English Frames: Genre

Formal Letters

— Key Points and Advice —

When writing a formal letter, you should:

◆ set out the letter to impress the reader
◆ make the purpose of your letter clear
◆ explain your points in detail
◆ write in connected sentences and paragraphs
◆ use an appropriate tone
◆ end your letter with a suitable conclusion.

Read the following points carefully before you apply them to the given title or exam question.

1. To start, always put **your address** at the **top right hand side** of the paper.
2. Put the **date** underneath your address.
3. On the **next line** down but **on the left hand side** of the paper, put the **name and address** of the **person to whom** you are writing.
4. Beneath their name and address:
   ● if you do not know their name, begin 'Dear Sir' or 'Dear Madam'
   ● if you know the name, begin 'Dear (name)'.
   Example:

9 Drury Avenue
Bolton
BL1 7KB

30 August 2000

Mr Baker
4 Waterstone Road
Wakefield
West Yorkshire
WF2 8HV

Dear Mr Baker,

5. Then begin the letter.
6. Set out the main purpose of your letter in the first sentence.
7. Ensure that paragraphs are used throughout the letter.
8. If you began 'Dear (name)', end 'Yours sincerely,'; if you began 'Dear Sir', end 'Yours faithfully,'.
   Remember:
   With magnets, <u>s</u>outh poles do not go together; with letters, 'Dear <u>S</u>ir,' and 'Yours <u>s</u>incerely,' do not go together.
9. Sign your name beneath 'Yours sincerely,' or 'Yours faithfully,'.
10. For clarity, write your name legibly beneath the signature.

Formal Letters

Practising Layouts

Name: _____ Date: _____

Set out the openings and endings for the following letters.

1. A letter to Tony Blair, The Houses of Parliament, Westminster, London SW1A 2TT.

Dear

Yours   ,

2. A letter to the manager of a local supermarket, whose name you do not know (invent the address).

Dear

Yours   ,

GCSE English Frames: Genre   © Folens (copiable page)

Formal Letters

Letter Content

Name: _____ Date: _____

It is essential that you:
- plan your letter: brainstorm, then organise the ideas
- always keep the title in mind – be aware of whether you are writing to:
- argue, persuade, instruct, inform, explain or describe.

Always follow the same pattern:
- **paragraph 1:** explain why you are writing
- **following paragraphs:** write the things you have to say – in detail
- **final paragraph:** sum up your message.

Useful Phrases

Here is a palette of the sorts of phrases that might be useful for a formal letter writing task. In each case, they use a formal tone to address the reader.

Openings
I felt I had to write in response to the letter you sent me ...
I am writing in order to ...
I find myself in the happy position of writing to let you know that ...
This letter is intended to ...

Linking Phrases/Discourse Markers
To support your viewpoint:
what is more ...
in addition ...
contrary to what you might have heard ...
furthermore ...

Endings
I look forward to hearing from you ...
I shall look forward to receiving ...
I hope that you will find time to reply ...
I have no doubt that you will wish to consider the matter further ...

To show you have considered another viewpoint:
of course, it is clear that ...
while some believe ...
I admit that ...
although ...

To hammer home your message:
so it is obvious, therefore, that ...
without question ...
the conclusion must be ...
there can be no doubt that ...

Formal Letters

A Writing Frame

Name: _____ Date: _____

Use the following frame to write a letter to your headteacher, to persuade him/her to allow the school to spend a full day raising money for charity.

Dear

On behalf of the vast majority of students at your school, I am writing

Contrary to what some people believe

We have various proposals.

First, we could

Second,

We hope, therefore, that you will be able to support

Yours

GCSE English Frames: Genre   © Folens (copiable page)

Formal Letters

A Model Letter

Name: _____ Date: _____

Fill in the missing words or phrases in this letter.

Dear   ,

On behalf of the vast majority of students at your school, I am writing to   you to
consider allowing us one day each year to   money for   . We feel
that this would be a   of the school year, and although we would miss a day's
formal schooling, the benefits to students, the school and the needy would be

Contrary to what some people believe, young people do care about   . We would
like to   to support Christian Aid, Oxfam, Save the Children
and Action Aid. These are all charities which the school has   in the past
and we know that they would be delighted with any extra funds we could raise.

We have various proposals for money-raising events. We would like to organise a
               ; we would like to be sponsored to clean up the area immediately around the school
(a plan that would be   the local   ); we would ask parents
and friends to sponsor us to paint   that are in need of improvement;
and in the evening we want to put on a charity concert, featuring local
as well as the winners of our school's talent competition.

We are sure the benefits arising from such a day will   for any
lost lesson time. Since students, community and charities will all benefit, this will contribute
massively to the school's

We hope, therefore, that you will be able to support our ideas and that you will give us a
positive   in the near   .

Yours sincerely,

Key Points and Advice

Speeches should:

◆ be well organised
◆ be written to be spoken out loud to an audience
◆ employ language to engage and sustain the audience's attention.

They often use:

◆ humour, including irony
◆ anecdotes, to prove points.

Read the following points carefully before you apply them to the given title or exam question.

1. Write appropriately for your audience.

2. Plan your ideas as for any other writing task. Use paragraphs.

3. In the first paragraph, introduce the purpose of your speech.

4. In the rest of the speech:
   ● clarify your viewpoint
   or/and
   ● build through to a climax.

5. Address the audience directly: e.g. 'ladies and gentlemen', 'you', 'we'.

6. Use rhetorical questions, which challenge the listener but do not expect a direct response: e.g. 'How can we sit around and allow these things to happen?'

7. Use repetition, contrast, 'pattern of three' ideas, etc. to make a point strongly: e.g. 'He can hide his head. He can pretend he does not understand. He can fool those around him. Yet he cannot fool himself.'

8. Use irony to mock people or situations. In this case, irony is when you say one thing but mean the opposite: e.g. 'She spends hours of her time telling people how to behave properly. Then, in a fit of temper, she smashes her neighbour's window. Still, I am sure we would not criticise her for that ...'

9. If appropriate, use a short sentence to shock, surprise or add emphasis: e.g. 'One thing that I am pretty sure about is that, for a headteacher, he held some points of view you would never expect, and which made you wonder how he ever got his job. For example, he hated assemblies. He also disapproved of homework. He said he hated school.'

10. The final paragraph should sum up your message.

    GCSE English Frames: Genre   © Folens (copiable page)

 **Speech Writing**

Practising Techniques

Name: _____ Date: _____

You have been told to write a speech to be given to your English group, in which you describe how you feel the school could be improved. You must not mention any particular members of staff!

1. Write **three** rhetorical questions you might include.
E.g. 'Surely we do not need to wear uniform?'

> 1.
>
> 2.
>
> 3.

2. Write **two** sets of sentences in which you use repetition or contrast for effect.
E.g. 'We slave away at school. We slave away at home. We slave away during the holidays. There is no end to our suffering.'

> 1.
>
>
> 2.

3. Write **two** sentences or extracts which use irony.
E.g. 'No student has a bad word to say about anything at school. Everyone believes it is a joy to be here. We don't mind if the wind blows through the windows. We are happy when the old wooden chairs ladder our tights ...'

> 1.
>
>
> 2.

4. Write **one** extract in which a short sentence is used for effect.
E.g. 'My first ever day at this school was frightening and it took me a long time to get over how upset I had felt when I returned home that night. I cried.'

> 1.

The Structure of the Speech

Name: _____   Date: _____

1. The Opening

Grab the attention of the listener.
You can use:
- an anecdote to bring a situation into focus
- a clear statement of what you believe
- an attack on the point of view with which you do not agree.

2. The Main Body of the Speech

To convince the audience, you should:
- move through a series of relevant points, linking them with discourse markers such as:
  what is more ...
  furthermore ...
  in addition ...
  of course, that is not all ...
  to make matters worse ...
- try to write a speech which becomes increasingly convincing, perhaps saving your best points until the end. You might need phrases like:
  Worst of all ...
  Most worrying is ...
  Of course, the best part of this was ...
  The highlight had to be ...
- consider using rhetoric, repetition, contrast, irony and surprise, effectively but sparingly.

3. The Ending

Either:
- sum up what you have said, making clear your own viewpoint: e.g. 'And, as we examine all this evidence, one thing is very clear – this situation cannot and must not be allowed to continue.'

Or:
- use repetition or rhetoric (or both) to create a climax: e.g. 'The law is perfectly correct. Those who oppose it are absolutely wrong. Those who must police it are doing their best. Who in this world could convince us that any change would be an improvement?'

Or:
- more subtly, leave the audience to make its own decision: e.g. 'You must decide, ladies and gentlemen, though as far as I can see the remedy is obvious. I wonder, are we brave enough to do what needs to be done?'

GCSE English Frames: Genre

A Writing Frame

Name: _____ Date: _____

Write the text of a speech to be given to a national conference for school children. You must argue that the village, town or city in which you live is an ideal place in which to grow up.

Fellow students, I am delighted to be able to talk to you today

There are many wonderful places in this country

However,   , where I live, is undoubtedly the ideal place in which to grow up, because

It has so much more to offer. For instance

In addition, the people are

More than anything, I love

To sum up, then: I am lucky to have been brought up in

Speech Writing

A Model Answer

Name: _____ Date: _____

Fill in the missing words or phrases in this speech.

Fellow students, I am delighted to have been invited to talk to you today. I am
because it gives me the chance to talk about Leeds, the   in which I live. It was a
marvellous place in which to be a child; and it is the   where I hope
to spend the rest of my

Of course, there are many   places in this country. I admit I have missed
the joys of   in the Lake District: I could have passed many hours bird-watching
and staggering up mountains in a force ten   . And I   I have missed
listening to the choir in Canterbury Cathedral and rowing down the river at Stratford. Instead,
I was wasting my time in the buzz of the   city.

Does that   me? No. I don't   it for a moment!

That is because the city in which I live is the ideal place in which to grow up. It has, for
instance, all the shops and   you could ever   . I was once approached
by a tourist, who was holding a map of the town and looking   baffled. He was
trying to find the   to the cinema. Unfortunately, it was hard to help him, because he had
no idea which cinema he was looking for. He had so much culture from which to
As well as the cinemas, there are clubs and theatres, and museums   art galleries.
We are also lucky to have such   parks and open spaces.

In addition, the people are the   you could hope to find. The old men
might wear flat caps and we might sometimes be a week behind in the latest fashions, but
everyone feels   . Streets feel like communities. People still support their
neighbours. When troubles do   – and, like everywhere else in England, drugs and
poverty are problems – at least   is trying to help.

More than anything, though, I   the sport. Football, cricket, athletics, and rugby are
all part of my life. Children can get top class coaching and spectators   watch
top class sportsmen and women, week in,   out.

To sum up, then: most of you will not have had the advantages I have enjoyed over the past
sixteen years. I come from a city that is   ; a city that is vibrant; a city that
                   after its own and welcomes new faces; a city which, I feel,   be matched
for friendship, entertainment and, in its own way, beauty. I recommend you
Leeds soon. But, be prepared –   won't want to leave.

GCSE English Frames: Genre   © Folens (copiable page)

Instructions

Key Points and Advice

Instructions should be:

◆ clear
◆ in a logical order
◆ appropriate for the target audience
◆ telling the reader what to do.

Read the following points carefully before you apply them to the given title or exam question.

1. Decide which method to use to set out the instructions. The methods available include:
   - a numbered list of points
   - sub-headings, followed by bullet points
   - sub-headings followed by short paragraphs
   - continuous writing.
2. Organise your ideas, with:
   - a general structure
   - points organised within each sub-section.
3. Often, it will be appropriate to include an introduction to the subject before moving to your first sub-heading. The introduction might:
   - say why the instructions are necessary
   - indicate what areas will be covered and why.
4. In the instructions, rely on the imperative tone, so you **tell** readers what to do. E.g. '**Go** to the bank ..., **Empty** the till ...'.
5. Use language that is suitable for the target audience. Remember that different kinds of people express themselves in different ways.
6. Stick with the given purpose of your instructions. Don't wander from the topic.
7. Use examples to support your points when appropriate. E.g. 'Have a fast car waiting around the corner, such as a Lotus, a Cosworth , or a super-charged Clio ...'.
8. Use illustrations to clarify points when appropriate. E.g.

 No cycling

9. Limit instructions to a suitable length – no more than three sides. Succinct instructions, which are relatively brief but to the point, are sometimes the best.
10. Move to a definite ending. You are likely to use phrases such as:
    - *Finally ...*
    - *If you follow these instructions ...*
    - *It is essential that you follow these instructions if you wish ...*
    - *These instructions should ensure you have ...*

Instructions

Practising Tone and Structure

Name: _____ Date: _____

1. Re-write the following instructions for an adult audience.

a) Don't freak out if stopped by the Bill.

_____

b) Tell it for real when questioned.

_____

c) Stay cool if they lean on you.

_____

2. Below is part of the general framework for a set of instructions that advises the public on how to behave at a swimming pool. Fill in the missing details below each sub-heading.

1. On arrival
- Check
-
-
-

2. When in the pool
- Behave sensibly at all times.
-
-
-
-

3. Advice about diving
- Only dive at the deep end.
- When using the diving boards
-
-

GCSE English Frames: Genre © Folens (copiable page)

Instructions

Developing Instructions

Name: _____ Date: _____

In examinations, moving beyond using only bullet points can help you gain higher marks, because writing in paragraphs lets you show how well you can join together your ideas.

It is, therefore, worth considering using sub-headings with a paragraph under each one, rather than just bullet points.

1. A Logical Order

A logical order for your ideas is essential, as ever, when using this method.

2. Discourse Markers

Discourse markers are also vital:
- *Then ...*
- *Following this ...*
- *Next ...*
- *It is essential that ...*
- *After you have ...*

3. The Imperative Tone

The imperative tone must be maintained.
Remember that you are giving instructions, not discussing an issue.

Your verbs must tell the reader what to do:
- *You must ensure that you ...*
- *Whatever happens, do not ...*
- *Make sure you follow this advice because ...*
- *Always remember ...*
- *Avoid ...*

4. Linking Sentences

Linking sentences in a paragraph gives you the opportunity to link your ideas effectively:

How to behave in the theatre
When we arrive, it is essential that you remember you are representing the school. Do not misbehave in any way. Make sure that you treat other members of the audience with respect and that you are projecting the image we expect. In particular, this means that shirts must be tucked in and chewing gum will not be allowed. Also, do not chatter or unwrap sweets during the performance. Ensure that you follow these instructions, otherwise you are unlikely to be welcomed on any other English trip.

Instructions

A Writing Frame

Name: _____ Date: _____

**Write a set of instructions for a family who have not been camping before.
Use the sub-heading and paragraph method. Advise them about:**

- **what to take**
- **where to camp**
- **camp-site rules**
- **facilities**
- **how to get the most out of the holiday.**

> When you are setting out on a camping holiday

> **1. What to take**
> Without the correct equipment, camping can be a nightmare, so take

> **2. Where to camp**
> Whenever possible, stay at a proper site, because

> **3. Camp-site rules**
> Always follow the rules

> **4. Facilities**
> Most camp-sites have a range of facilities. Always treat them with respect. For instance

> **5. How to get the most out of your holiday**
> Finally, to enjoy a camping holiday, don't expect the sort of life-style you get in a hotel

GCSE English Frames: Genre

 *Instructions*

A Model Answer

Name: _____ Date: _____

Fill in the missing words or phrases in this set of instructions.

When you are setting out on a   holiday, it is important that you are well and know what to expect. Like on any other   , you want to have a good   , so follow these instructions and you won't go far wrong!

1. What to take
Without the correct equipment, camping can be a   , so take all the important items with   . Obviously, you will take a tent; but don't forget the sleeping bags,   , camping stove and matches, tent, torch and   on. Before you set off, think carefully through what a   day might be like, and   down all the things you will need. For example, remember to   a toilet roll! Without one, you   be heading for disaster!

2. Where to camp
Whenever possible, stay at a registered site,   it is likely to be better maintained. If you are allowed to   a place to pitch your tent, make sure it is flat and not too   from the water supply and the toilets. Also, always leave a distance   your tent and your neighbours', because tents do not   out unwelcome noise.

3. Camp-site rules
Always follow the rules. Each site will have its own, but they have   in common. For instance, if you have a   , it must be under control at all times; if you have children, so must   ! Avoid upsetting other campers. In particular, make no   after sunset and remember that many people will want to   until eight or nine o'clock in the morning.

4. Facilities
Many camp-sites have toilets and shower blocks,   up facilities and some form of laundry room. Always leave these   in the state you found them. Living as part of such a large community, you must   others. If there is a camp shop, do not be   if the prices are higher than elsewhere. You might find it more economical to shop in the nearest   or village and use the camp shop only for   .

5. How to get the most out of your holiday
Finally, to enjoy a camping holiday, do not expect the sort of life-style you get in a hotel. If it is   and there is mud everywhere, laugh about it. Do not worry! Everything will dry out   . If you spill your food on to the grass, it is not the end of the   : camping is about taking things in your   . And if you manage to have a typical camping holiday, you will   want to have another!

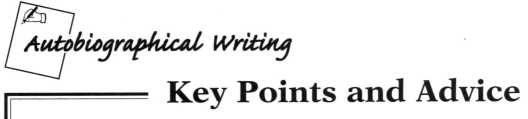

Autobiographical Writing

Key Points and Advice

Autobiographical writing usually presents:

◆ a subjective view of life, i.e. things are seen from the writer's viewpoint
◆ original descriptions, i.e. incidents are re-told or things described in a new way; and are related to the thoughts or feelings of the writer
◆ detailed accounts.

Read the following points carefully before you apply them to the given title or exam question.

1. Whether you are writing to inform, explain or describe, always plan your writing carefully. Start with an unusual or exciting opening, to interest the reader.

2. Write about what you know. Stories that are totally invented are unlikely to seem realistic. Use your five senses to make the description sharp and the situation convincing.

3. Present a view which is clearly your own.

4. Your writing is likely to be less formal. Because the writing is about yourself, you may use the terms 'I' and 'we' more often than in some other forms of writing. Also, abbreviations are more likely to be used ('wouldn't', 'can't', etc.).

5. Just because you are writing about yourself, do not limit the range of your vocabulary to the sort of words you would say to a close friend. In examinations, you are assessed on your ability to use a wide vocabulary.

6. Use speech to clarify or illustrate situations.

7. Consider using similes or metaphors to bring originality to your response:
   e.g. *My brother is like an angel* – simile.
       My sister is a tiger – metaphor.

8. Your writing is likely to be based on anecdotes (short, personal stories that make a point).

9. Use humour, where appropriate, to add interest.

10. End your writing effectively. Do not allow the response to just fade away. Since your ending is the last thing the marker will read before giving you a mark or grade, make sure that it is interesting.

GCSE English Frames: Genre © Folens (copiable page)

 *Autobiographical Writing*

Improving Autobiographical Writing

Name: _____ Date: _____

Think of the most exciting thing you have ever done.

1. Write **three similes** that reveal how you felt.

- It made me feel like

- For that moment, I was as

-

2. Write **three metaphors** that reveal how you felt.

-

-

-

3. Write a brief conversation that brings part of the incident to life.
   If no one else was involved, re-tell part of what happened to someone else, beginning like this:
   "Was it really exciting?" Sarah asked.
   "Oh, yes," I replied ...

```



```

4. Write a brief humorous description of the incident, or of part of the incident.
   If it was not funny at the time, no doubt some aspect of it, such as how you felt or how you
   behaved, seems amusing now.

```



```

Autobiographical Writing

Structuring a Response

Name: _____ Date: _____

When you write about yourself, you usually have much to say.
One main problem, therefore, is that the available ideas have to be edited, so that you:
- use what is most suitable
- do not include irrelevant material.

You should:
- resist the temptation to simply fill page after page with incidents or descriptions
- plan your response carefully.

1. The Opening

You can begin by saying what your response will be about. However, unusual, exciting or lively openings are more likely to impress the reader.

Consider beginning with:
- an anecdote
- an argument or conversation
- a series of controversial comments
- a description
- or anything unexpected.

Then move on to a more logical discussion of the given title. Your opening will have already given an impression of your point of view.

2. The Central Section

Having brainstormed your topic, you should have selected the story you are going to tell, or the incidents you are going to deal with. It is sensible to choose a relatively short story or two or three incidents, because then you can deal with them in depth.

When planning:
- put your ideas into a sensible order, so that one leads logically to the next
- do not limit each idea to just one paragraph: some might need more.

Use discourse markers:
- *On another occasion ...*
- *That's not all ...*
- *On the other hand ...*
- *However ...*

3. The Ending

Depending upon the purpose of your writing, consider using:
- a summary of the message in your response
- your honest point of view
- a final and relevant anecdote
- a rhetorical question to challenge the reader: e.g. 'I think there must be better ways of spending our life than this, don't you?'

GCSE English Frames: Genre

Autobiographical Writing

A Writing Frame

Name: _____ Date: _____

Describe the time in your life when you were most afraid.

I am not usually afraid of anything, but I was terrified

It all started when

As if things were not bad enough

Of course, the next thing that happened was

By the end

When I look back on it all, I can't help thinking that

Autobiographical Writing

A Model Response

Name: _____ Date: _____

Fill in the missing words or phrases in the response below.

Fear can grip you so that it's hard to move or even think. It can _____ your brain so that you seem, in a way, to have no feelings. Yet your _____ pounds as if it might thump right out of your chest. You are there and yet not there. It is the _____ sheep must have, when their lorry pulls up outside the slaughter house.

I was _____ like that as I sat in the dentist's waiting room. The _____ of antiseptic and mouthwash were just as usual, and there was the usual clinking and drilling, but I was not there for a checkup or a _____. My teeth were bleeding and my top lip was cut and swollen. One of my front _____ was knocked up and bent round. The _____ one was fractured across.

The receptionist had told me to wait. The _____ would see me _____.

When, _____, I was sitting in the smooth black chair, I felt no better. I explained about the fall and how I had _____ on my teeth and about the pain.

"This is interesting," he said, _____ my teeth. Interesting was not the word that came to my mind. "I think," he said, "that we can sort this out. With a bit of luck, we'll be _____." I would have preferred not to be relying on luck. "Let me tell you what _____ going to do," he continued. "I'll take off the piece of broken tooth – it's fractured _____ to the gum-line – and I'm going to fit a kind of spike into it, then _____ it back on to what is left of the tooth. It might well stick." 'Might' was a _____ that did not appeal, either.

There followed the _____ of the injections. Four to begin with: up the front, so it _____ as if the needle was coming out of my nose. Then, when they didn't _____, another six into the roof of my mouth. "Brace yourself, this won't be too bad and it will all be _____ in a few seconds," was a lie.

I think dental nurses kept _____ and going, but I was in a painful daze. It was not because of what he started doing to my teeth. Soon, my mouth was _____, so I felt nothing.

It was more to do with the fact that I started to _____ the horror of what had happened. I was fourteen years old and my _____ were a mess. The teeth that were supposed to last me a lifetime were _____. This was a new fear. I was afraid of _____ laughed at; afraid of having _____ girlfriends; afraid of having no teeth at all.

_____ I came out of the dentist's, the tooth was stuck back for the _____, but I was still afraid – of _____ was to come.

GCSE English Frames: Genre © Folens (copiable page)

 **Leaflets**

Key Points and Advice

Leaflets are usually:

◆ designed to attract and hold the reader's attention
◆ intended to be persuasive
◆ concise, i.e. they do not wander from their purpose.

They often contain:

◆ rhetorical questions, to challenge the reader
◆ emotive language, which touches the emotions of the reader
◆ illustrations
◆ text boxes full of facts or opinions.

Read the following points carefully before you apply them to the given title or exam question.

1. Take care to plan your leaflet with the required purpose and audience in mind.
2. Having brainstormed your topic, be selective in which ideas you use. Leaflets are often only two sides long.
3. Create an effective title or headline:
   ● keep it relatively short
   ● consider the use of alliteration, to make it memorable:
   e.g. 'Ban Boring Uniforms'
        'Schools Slow to Change'.
4. Write a first paragraph to catch the reader's attention.
5. Use language which is appropriate for the audience:
   e.g. (for adults) Schools should be more aware of youngsters' life-styles
        (for teenagers) Schools need to get a grip on what's happening on the street.
6. Columns can make the leaflet look more professional.
7. Sub-headings can guide readers through the text and lead them to your most important points:
   e.g. 'Ties must go'
        'Trainers sharper than shoes'.
8. Use text boxes, illustrations, graphs, etc. to highlight important aspects.
9. Try to end with a clear message:
   e.g. 'School students have a right to make their voices heard. After all, school is there for them, not for their parents. Students know that uniforms should be banned and as support for change grows, schools will have to listen.'
10. Consider including a reply slip for those who require further information or wish to make a donation.

Practising Leaflet Techniques

Name: _____ Date: _____

Design a leaflet to convince people that we should all do more to help the police preserve law and order.

1. Create two headlines for the leaflet:

aimed at teenagers

```
[                                                                    ]
```

aimed at adults

```
[                                                                    ]
```

2. Sketch a layout for the leaflet (single sheet), using one of your titles plus columns, boxes and an illustration.

3. Write an opening paragraph for teenagers. Assume they would not normally be interested in this topic.
Begin:

> Helping the police isn't the item at the top of most teenagers' lists of 'what to do during the holidays'! However, if someone broke into your house and stole your music system

Leaflets

Leaflet Style

Name: _____ Date: _____

1. Facts and Opinions

Leaflets will usually be a mixture of facts and opinions.
Remember:
- facts can be proved
- opinions are what somebody thinks.
Sometimes, opinions will be disguised as facts, to persuade the reader that a point of view is correct.
E.g. 'Many women hate cooking' – opinion
Up to 75% of women are believed to hate cooking' – apparent fact: but notice the phrase 'are believed to', which is not offering genuine proof.

2. Language

Leaflets use a variety of techniques to influence the reader.
These include:
- rhetorical questions
- emotive language:
e.g. 'Picture the poor husband, trapped for hours in the kitchen because his wife cannot be bothered to cook ...'
'Society has somehow produced an unfeeling, cruel male sex which drives the women into the kitchen ...'

3. Discourse Markers

Ideas have to be joined together. In persuasive leaflets, you are likely to use discourse markers, such as:
What is more ...
In addition ...
Furthermore ...
Even more serious is ...
Contributing to this situation ...

4. Text Boxes

Clusters of facts or opinions will often be placed in boxes, to stand out from the rest of the text. There are likely to be only one or two of these on each page, for maximum impact.

5. Illustrations

When used, illustrations can:
- clarify a point of view – by presenting the idea in a cartoon form
- attack opposing points of view – by making them appear ridiculous.

Leaflets

A Writing Frame

Name: _____ Date: _____

Produce a leaflet to be given to parents thinking of sending their children to your school. The leaflet should persuade them it would be a good choice.

Parents never regret sending their children to

In addition, the school's examination results

The school has so many excellent features

Outstanding facilities

The school is best known for its

Indeed, sending your son or daughter to _____ School is likely to be the best decision you have ever made. We are confident

Three good reasons to choose _____ School

-
-
-

    GCSE English Frames: Genre   © Folens (copiable page)

 *Leaflets*

A Model Leaflet

Name: _____ Date: _____

Fill in the missing words or phrases.

A school that   the charts

There are certain decisions which are so _____ they cannot be left to chance. And _____ things are as important as the choice of a high school for your _____. After all, what happens between the ages of 11 and 16 will _____ that student for the rest of their life.

_____ parents look for the best, they come to Alnay School. We offer a _____ of extra-curricular activities which is second to none, have a pastoral system that other _____ seek to copy and produce _____ results which are first class.

We are the proof that comprehensive _____ works.

> **We offer:**
> - high quality teaching
> - a supportive learning environment
> - a range of _____ teams
> - after-school clubs _____ evening
> - a reputation which is _____ to none.

We feel that our _____ publicity comes from our past students. Their successes provide an _____ for what we achieve.

Awards

_____, in addition, we have recently been presented with two curriculum awards _____ the government. Also, we have _____ a glowing report from the OFSTED

inspectors. They said, "This is a _____ of which the town can be proud."

Examination Successes

The inspectors noted the _____ that almost 90% of our students _____ five A*–C grades at GCSE; and that our percentage of A* grades is _____ the best in the county.

When this is added to the fact that we _____ provided two _____ of the England Under-16 Football Team last year, as well as a girl who _____ for the Senior Great Britain Women's Ice Hockey Team, you get an idea of the skills training we _____.

Your Best

We believe that sending your child to Alnay School will prove the best decision you have _____ made. That is _____ we care for individuals and teach them how to _____ as part of a community, as well as _____ them on to success.

Why would you consider accepting second _____ when Alnay School is offering so much more?

> **What parents say:**
> - "My child is _____ and learning so much"
> - "It's the education I _____ I'd had"
> - "I'd _____ school to anyone"

 *Travel Brochures*

Key Points and Advice

Brochures usually:

◆ describe a product
◆ give a positive impression of the product.

Travel brochures:

◆ advertise holiday destinations
◆ give details of the resort
◆ set out to attract visitors.

Read the following points carefully before you apply them to the given title or exam question.

1. Write about a place you know well or know a great deal about. Then, your description will be more convincing.
2. Brainstorm around your destination. Then organise the details carefully, producing a logical sequence for the information (e.g. give a description of the destination before you mention hotels, etc.).
3. Design a layout, using pictures when appropriate, and possibly columns and sub-headings.
4. Begin and end your description strongly.
5. Aim your description at your target audience – for example, the attractions that teenagers will be looking for are different to those sought by old people.
6. Stress the positive aspects of a place and avoid negative comments.
7. Develop phrases that give a positive impression, to support the more usual discourse markers.
   E.g. use similes: 'it is like paradise on earth'
   　　　　　　　　　'the waves crash like volcanic eruptions on to the beach'
8. Consider the range of attractions:
   ● beaches
   ● climate
   ● historical sites
   ● people
   ● entertainment
   ● accommodation.
9. Consider using particular marketing techniques:
   e.g. 'This holiday is the cheapest you will find.'
   　　　'This holiday is expensive. That is because you are paying for excellence.'
10. Add additional details such as the cost of accommodation, car hire, etc., if time and space allow.

 *Travel Brochures*

Practising Planning

Name: _____   Date: _____

Produce a travel brochure to attract families to a holiday resort of your choice. Inform them of its attractions.

BRAINSTORM

Hotels

RESORT

Plan

Organise your ideas into a sensible order.

1. Exciting opening.

2.

3.

4.

5.

6.

7.

8.

9.

10. Ending that mentions all the best features again.

Sketch the design for a page

Include a headline, possibly columns, and an indication of what pictures you would use.

Travel Brochures

Improving the Style

Name: _____ Date: _____

1. Openings

Use a descriptive phrase as a headline:
e.g. 'Corfu, a little England in Greece'
Then, the first paragraph must interest the reader. Use:
- general statements about what the place has to offer
- a description of the place, perhaps at a certain time of day
- an explanation of what sorts of people go there

or
- an explanation of why people go there.

2. Language

Often, the language is exciting, romantic or welcoming, depending on the place and the target audience. However, phrasing is almost always positive:
This is a holiday destination beyond your wildest dreams
People return year after year
It is impossible to capture in words the beauty of sunsets over the mountains
Since Roman times, this has been an island for lovers
Every member of the family is catered for

3. Discourse Markers

These, too, will be positive:
- *In addition*
- *What's more*
- *That's not all*
- *Come what may*

4. Relevant Details

As you deal with accommodation, special features, climate etc., you must decide whether simply to include them in your description or to use one or two text boxes.

5. Pictures

Pictures, too, should be used sparingly. If you are creating a brochure in an examination, do not waste time trying to produce a perfect picture. A quick sketch will be enough.

Your marks are awarded for your English ability; extra credit might be gained for good layout, but not for artistic ability.

6. Ending

Aim to leave a lasting impression, with either:
- a final vivid description
- a plea for people to 'discover' this wonderful place

or
- a re-cap of its best features.

GCSE English Frames: Genre

Travel Brochures

A Writing Frame

Name: _____ Date: _____

**Produce a travel brochure to attract families to a holiday resort of your choice.
Inform them of its attractions.**

Of all the places in the world, this must be the best

Each day is a kind of perfection

You will find the people so friendly

There is so much to see and do

Whether you choose to stay in a hotel or opt for self-catering

If you are looking for the holiday of a lifetime, you need look no further

Travel Brochures

A Model Answer

Name: _____ Date: _____

Fill in the missing words or phrases.

Folegandros is the island of your

Your holiday on Folegandros will be unforgettable, because Folegandros is Greece as it   to be. You will be   from fast food and discos.   , you will be alone with the sea and the sun and peace.

Sitting   an emerald in the Aegean Sea, Folegandros is virtually cut off from the of the Greek Islands. It is visited by only a handful of boats   week. It is majestic and mountainous, peopled by islanders who   little English but who are kind, courteous and honest. They welcome visitors as their   and grandparents did: they will give you and drink and talk for hours   their lives. Don't worry if you don't speak the language – friendliness of this   speaks an international language.

A paradise for

The sea is crystal clear and   for bathing. Your children will adore its warm waters, which are   with fish. While you lie back and admire the views, your children   be occupied with net and line. And don't worry if the locals join them in their fun – the   love children too!

The beaches are made of clean, smooth pebbles, but don't   to be offered a sun-lounger. If you travel back in time to a golden age like this, you have to   your own comforts. So, pack beach towels and an   to keep off the sun. Also, bring lots of sun lotion, just in case the three local shops   !

Whatever happens, the tavernas will have   of good food and wine, so your evenings will provide the sort of atmosphere you   existed only in the movies. As the sun drops the horizon's rim, and leaves the world to old Greek philosophers and a night   of crickets, you will stroll off to sleep the deep sleep of a soul that is   relaxed.

It's now or never!

Sadly, the world will   , and Folegandros will be overtaken by tourists. It cannot remain such a secret   .

If you want to enjoy all it has to offer, visit it now, before it is too   . It is a unique island, a glimpse back at   life used to be and how, perhaps, it should be.

                    paradise now, before it is lost!